Usborne Workbook
Comprehension

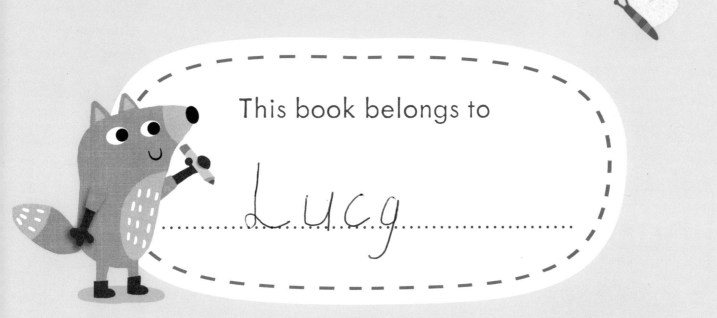

This book belongs to

Lucy

There are answers on page 27, and notes for grown-ups at the back of the book.

Here are some of the woodland animals you'll meet in this book.
Use a pen or pencil to complete the phrases on their cards.

Olly the owl

Once

upon

a

time

Mo the mouse

Foxy the fox

Can you trace the missing words?

Moley the mole

happily

ever

after

Spike the hedgehog

Stripe the badger

Squilly the squirrel

Help the animals with their comprehension skills in this book.
You can draw, trace and write on each page.

Usborne Workbooks
Comprehension

Illustrated by Anna Süßbauer

Written by Hannah Watson
Designed by Keith Newell

You may need to help your child read the instructions in this book.

big bad Wolf

Bun the rabbit

Coco the raccoon

There are extra pages for more practice at the back of the book.

Hug the bear

Edited by Kristie Pickersgill
Series Editor: Felicity Brooks

Reading labels

The animals want to write some signs to label things in the wood where they live. Trace and copy the words they have thought of on the list below.

tree   tree   tree

rock   rock   rock

gate   gate   gate

pond   pond   Pond

Help the animals complete their signs. Choose the correct word from the opposite page to write on each one.

_t_ _r_ _e_ _e_

___ _____ _____ _____

__ _____ _____ _____ _____

_____ _____ _____ _____

Mo isn't sure what to put on her sign. Help her by choosing the best word from the white box. Write it on the line.

_____

frog

flower

flag

Lists

Spike and Stripe are going on holiday. Spike only needs to pack the things on his list. Draw lines from the things on the shelves to his suitcase and cross their names off the list.

Spike's things to pack

book

sunglasses

sandals

beach ball

Spike

Help Stripe finish her packing. Cross off the things on her list that she's already packed. Draw a circle around anything she's forgotten.

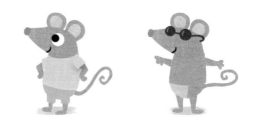

Stripe's holiday packing

teddy bear

towel

sunhat

sun cream

Do you think Spike and Stripe are going to a hot place or a cold place on holiday? Tick the correct box.

Now help Spike pack for a holiday in a <u>cold place</u>. Draw circles around the things on the shelves he should pack.

Simple sentences

The animals are talking about their toys. Read the sentences below, then draw a line to match each animal to the toy he or she is talking about.

Stripe's shop sells lots of different toys. Can you help her label them? Draw a string to match each label to the correct toy.

train   robot   boat   teddy bear

What kind of shop does Stripe have? Copy the shop words on to the empty signs. Then, draw a star next to the correct sign.

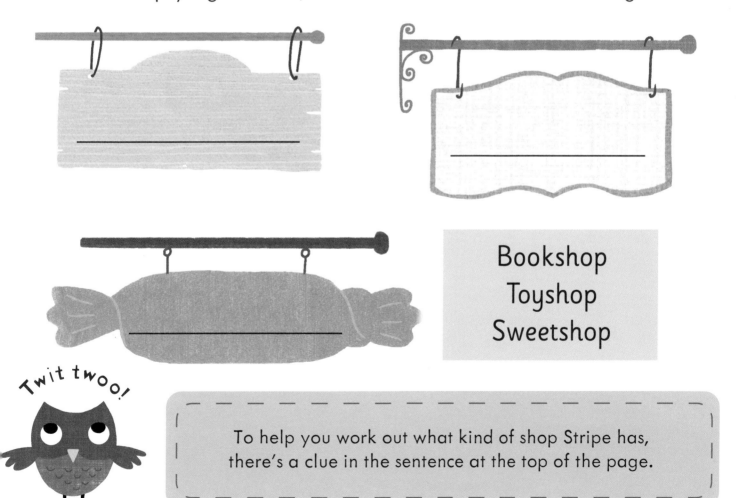

Bookshop
Toyshop
Sweetshop

Twit twoo!

To help you work out what kind of shop Stripe has, there's a clue in the sentence at the top of the page.

What comes next?

Foxy has written a story, but the pages are muddled. Write
1, 2, 3 or 4 in the small boxes to show the correct order of the pages.

A strong wind blew it out of my paws.

At last, I found it caught in a bush.

I took my kite to the park.

I looked everywhere for it.

Write a sentence about what might happen next in the story.

_____

_____

Think of some words to describe how Foxy felt when he found his kite. Write them below.

_____

_____

Reading instructions

Coco has written instructions for making a cake, but some steps are missing. Write the correct sentence from the green box in each space.

1. _____

_____

2. Measure the ingredients.

3. Mix everything together in a bowl.

4. _____

_____

Wash your hands.

Set a timer.

Pour the mixture into a tin.

Take the cake out of the oven.

What type of writing is Coco's set of instructions? Circle the answer.

a poem   a cake recipe   a fairy tale

Twit twoo!

Instructions and recipes tell you how to do something. They are often numbered so you know the order in which to do the steps.

5. Put the cake in the oven.

6. _____
_____

7. _____
_____

8. Let the cake cool, then ice it.

Draw some more cherries on top of my cake, please.

Finding information

Squilly, Spike and Mo have found a flower in the woods. Draw a circle around the information book that could help them find out more about the flower.

All About Trees

Flowers and Where They are Found

Guide to Forest Animals

Contents

Which page will help the animals learn more about the flower they found? Write the number in the box.

Which page will give the animals information about looking after flowers?

Twit twoo!

Information books are known as **nonfiction** books. This means they contain facts and are not made up.

Read these sentences about woodland flowers. Put a tick next to the sentence that best describes the flower the animals found.

bluebell - a blue flower with petals that look like bells.

daisy - a small white flower with a yellow centre.

foxglove - a tall flower with pink or purple petals.

Now, write a sentence describing this butterfly that Bun has seen. The words below could give you some ideas of things to talk about.

pattern   wings   colour   size

_____

_____

_____

Write a sentence about a time that you saw something exciting or special. Use this word list to help you.

amazing   surprise   happy   discover

_____

_____

Traditional tales

Twit twoo!

> Stories, poems and plays are known as **fiction.**
> This means they are made up. Traditional tales and fairy tales
> are well-known stories that have been retold lots of times.

Read the start of the story below, then answer the questions.

Little Red Riding Hood

"Grandma's ill in bed," said Little Red Riding Hood's
mother. "Will you take this basket of food to her?
Be sure to stay on the path. There's a big, bad wolf
in the forest."

Read the words below, then find and circle them in the text above.

| Grandma | food | path | forest |

Who is feeling ill in the story? Circle the correct picture.

Grandma

Little Red Riding Hood

Big, bad wolf

Little Red Riding Hood skipped through the thick forest. She soon forgot all about staying on the path. As she bent to pick some flowers, she heard a low growl. "Hello little girl," said the big, bad wolf.

What did Little Red Riding Hood stop to pick up?
Circle the correct picture.

books

food

flowers

surprised

scared

nervous

worried

Write a sentence to describe how Little Red Riding Hood might have felt when she met the wolf. Look at the words in the blue box to help you.

_____

_____

_____

Write a sentence about what you think might happen next in the story.

_____

_____

Familiar phrases

The animals are on a camping trip and they are telling stories around the campfire.

Choose a word from the signpost to finish each speech bubble. They are all phrases you may have heard before in stories.

Hug wants to write a story. Choose a word from the green box to write in each gap to help him think of some well-known characters.

| little | handsome | fairy | fierce |

The three _ _ _ _ _ _ pigs.

A _ _ _ _ _ godmother.

A _ _ _ _ _ _ _ _ prince.

A _ _ _ _ _ _ dragon.

Twit twoo!

A **character** is a person in a story, poem or play.
Animals can also be characters.

Reading poems

Twit twoo!

A **poem** is a piece of writing which often has a rhythm, and which sometimes rhymes. Nursery rhymes are poems.

Coco is reading a poem to Foxy. Try reading the poem below aloud, then do the activities on these pages.

Hey Diddle, Diddle

Hey diddle, diddle,

The cat and the fiddle,

The cow jumped over the moon;

The little dog laughed

To see such fun,

And the dish ran away

With the spoon.

Find and underline all the <u>animals</u> in the poem.

Hey diddle, diddle, the cat and the fiddle...

Draw a picture of any of the characters in the poem.

Who jumped over the moon in the poem?
Put a ring around the correct picture below.

Which words could you use to describe the dog in the poem?
Circle them below.

funny   silly   angry   sad   happy

Comprehension practice

Bun has written about her day in the forest.
Read the sentences she has written.

Dear Diary,

Today I played in the forest.

First I climbed a tree with Mo.

Then we built a den.

It rained, so we went home.

Now answer each question by circling the correct picture below.

Where did Bun play?

What kind of weather does Bun write about?

Bun has written another sentence about her day.

We ate carrots for supper.

Draw a picture on the plate of what Bun ate for supper.

What is your favourite meal?

Think about what you would like to eat for supper.
Then, write a sentence about it in the space below.

_____

What do you think Bun did after her supper?
Put a tick next to the correct picture.

got ready for bed

went to school

ate breakfast

Comprehension quiz

Find out how much you've learned about comprehension skills by doing this quiz. Answers on page 26.

1. Draw a line from each **label** below to the correct object.

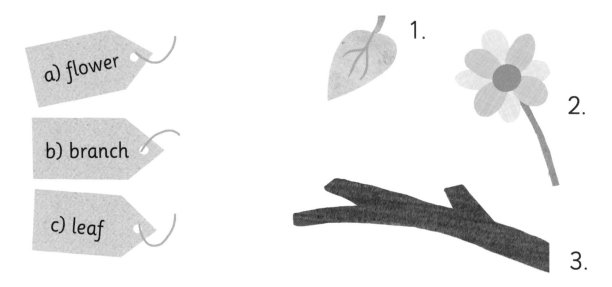

2. a) Bun has gone shopping. Draw a star next to the thing on her shopping list that she has forgotten to put in her basket.

b) Do you think Bun is going to make a fruit salad, or bake a cake? Put a tick in the correct box.

a fruit salad ☐   a cake ☐

3. Read the **sentence** below, then tick the correct box to answer the question.

"The fruit I like the best in my shop is watermelon," said Spike.

Where does Spike work?

a) a supermarket ☐   b) a bookshop ☐   c) a toyshop ☐

4. i) The order of Foxy's **story** below is muddled. Put the sentences in the right order by writing 1, 2, 3 or 4 in the boxes.

☐ a) I was playing football with Bun.

☐ b) Mum heard the crash and came over.

☐ c) Our ball broke my mum's flowerpot.

☐ d) Luckily, she wasn't angry as it was an accident.

ii) Put a tick next to the word that you think describes how Foxy felt when the ball broke the flowerpot.

happy ☐   worried ☐   bored ☐

5. Put a tick in the correct box to show whether each of these types of writing is **fiction** or **nonfiction**.

	fiction	nonfiction
a) recipe book	☐	☐
b) poem	☐	☐
c) fairy tale	☐	☐
d) information book	☐	☐

6. Draw a line to the correct word to complete the names of these **familiar fairy tale characters.**

a) The genie of the

b) Little Red Riding

c) The big, bad

lamp

wolf

Hood

Quiz answers

1. a) 2   b) 3   c) 1

2. a) pears   b) a fruit salad

3. a)

4. i) a) 1 b) 3 c) 2 d) 4   ii) worried

5. fiction: b, c   nonfiction: a, d

6. a) lamp b) Hood c) wolf

Score 1 point for each correct answer and write your score in this box: ____

18

Answers

Pages 4-5
Clockwise from top: gate, rock, pond, tree.   Mo's sign: flower

Pages 6-7
Spike needs to pack: Stripe has forgotten a <u>sunhat</u>.   For a <u>cold place</u>, Spike could pack:
   The animals are going to a <u>hot place</u>.

Pages 8-9

Foxy: Moley:

Spike: Coco:

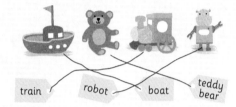

Stripe's shop is a <u>toyshop</u>.

train robot boat teddy bear

Pages 10-11
1: I took my kite to the park.   2: A strong wind blew it out of my paws.
3: I looked everywhere for it.   4: At last, I found it caught in a bush.
Foxy could: go home, fly his kite, play in the park, celebrate, feel happy.
Foxy could feel: happy, relieved, surprised, pleased, glad, lucky.

Page 12-13
Step 1: Wash your hands.   Step 6: Set a timer.   Coco's instructions
Step 4: Pour the mixture into a tin.   Step 7: Take the cake out of the oven.   are a <u>cake recipe</u>.

Pages 14-15
The book that will help the animals is 'Flowers and Where They are Found'.
<u>Page 14</u> will help them find out about their flower. <u>Page 26</u> will help them look after flowers.
The animals have found a <u>bluebell</u>.

Pages 16-17
<u>Grandma</u> is feeling ill.
Little Red Riding Hood stopped to pick <u>flowers</u>.

Pages 18-19
Once upon a <u>time</u>
In a kingdom far, far <u>away</u>   The three <u>little</u> pigs. A <u>fairy</u> godmother.
They all lived happily <u>ever</u> after.   A <u>handsome</u> prince. A <u>fierce</u> dragon.

Pages 20-21
The <u>cat</u> and the fiddle,   The <u>cow</u> jumped over the moon.
The <u>cow</u> jumped over the moon;   The dog could be: happy, silly, funny.
The little <u>dog</u> laughed

Pages 22-23
Bun played in the <u>forest</u>.
Bun writes about the <u>rain</u>.
After supper, Bun <u>got ready for bed</u>.

Don't worry if you made some mistakes. You can cross or rub out your answers and try again.

You can use these pages for extra comprehension practice.

I need to label the things in my shop.

Can you match these things to their labels, for Stripe?

sunglasses

ball

sandals

sun cream

It's so sunny. Let's go to the beach!

First, I need to go to the shops and buy some sunglasses.

After the beach, we should go to the café.

Phew. After all that, we'll need a nap!

Write about Spike's day. What was the weather like? Where did he go?

My grandma has long ears and a pink nose. She always wears a spotted scarf and carries a big handbag.

I love scarves too!

Can you draw a picture of Bun's grandma?

Can you help Mo draw a picture to go with the rhyme?

Hickory, dickory, dock

Hickory, dickory, dock,
The mouse ran up the clock.
The clock struck one,
The mouse ran down,
Hickory, dickory, dock.

Notes for grown-ups

Reading labels (pages 4-5)

To complete this activity, children must use essential comprehension skills such as reading a word, decoding and understanding it, and relating it to an object on the page. The use of labels is introduced, preparing children to understand their function in more complex pieces of writing.

Lists (pages 6-7)

Here, children must handle information presented as a list, and make logical decisions using it, e.g. predicting a holiday destination based on which words and items are associated with hot and cold places.

Simple sentences (pages 8-9)

On page 8, children locate key words within simple sentences to answer questions about favourite toys. Saying which shop might sell certain items on page 9 requires children to use inference, a crucial comprehension skill.

What comes next? (pages 10-11)

In this activity, children must decide the order of sentences in a short story. Suggest to children that clues in the text, such as when settings and characters are introduced, can help them make sense of the narrative order. Encourage children to think imaginatively about characters' emotions and about plot predictions.

Reading instructions (pages 12-13)

Instructions and recipes are introduced here as one type of nonfiction writing that children will be expected to recognize. The task of putting the recipe steps in order builds on the key comprehension skills of decoding information, matching captions to pictures and making predictions about which step comes next.

Finding information (pages 14-15)

Here, children learn how to handle information presented in nonfiction books, choosing the title and page number that will be most helpful to answer the questions. Children could look at other information books and spot some of the key features of nonfiction texts, such as contents pages, headings and labels.

Traditional tales (pages 16-17)

These pages introduce traditional tales and fairy tales as an important type of fiction writing that children will encounter. Children must find answers to traditional comprehension style questions in a more complex section of text. Children engage with the text by imagining characters' emotions and predicting what might come next.

Familiar phrases (pages 18-19)

Here, children focus on 'familiar phrases' from traditional stories that they will be expected to recognize and remember. You could help children think of other common phrases and well-known fairy tale characters.

Reading poems (pages 20-21)

This activity introduces poetry, in particular nursery rhymes, as another form of fiction writing that children will encounter. The questions check their understanding of the characters and narrative. Encourage children to read this and other favourite poems aloud to listen for the rhythms and rhyme schemes.

Comprehension practice (pages 22-23)

These pages recap the crucial comprehension skills and topics practised in the book. The questions check understanding, ask children for an imaginative response to the passage, and to predict what happens next.